SONGS FOR SOLO S

CHRISTINA AGUILERA

WISE PUBLICATIONS
PART OF THE MUSIC SALES GROUP

LONDON / NEW YORK / PARIS / SYDNEY / COPENHAGEN / BERLIN / MADRID / HONG KONG / TOKYO

PUBLISHED BY

WISE PUBLICATIONS
14-15 BERNERS STREET, LONDON W1T 3LJ, UK

EXCLUSIVE DISTRIBUTORS:

MUSIC SALES LIMITED
DISTRIBUTION CENTRE, NEWMARKET ROAD,
BURY ST EDMUNDS, SUFFOLK IP33 3YB, UK

MUSIC SALES PTY LIMITED
20 RESOLUTION DRIVE,
CARINGBAH, NSW 2229, AUSTRALIA

ORDER NO. AM999416
ISBN 978-1-84938-382-0
THIS BOOK © COPYRIGHT 2010 WISE PUBLICATIONS,
A DIVISION OF MUSIC SALES LIMITED.

EDITED BY LIZZIE MOORE.
CD RECORDED & PERFORMED BY PAUL HONEY.
CD RECORDED, MIXED & MASTERED BY JONAS PERSSON.
COVER DESIGNED BY LIZZIE BARRAND.

PHOTOGRAPHS:
ALL PHOTOS: © LFI

PRINTED IN THE EU

WWW.MUSICSALES.COM

YOUR GUARANTEE OF QUALITY
AS PUBLISHERS, WE STRIVE TO PRODUCE EVERY BOOK
TO THE HIGHEST COMMERCIAL STANDARDS.
THE MUSIC HAS BEEN FRESHLY ENGRAVED AND THE BOOK HAS
BEEN CAREFULLY DESIGNED TO MINIMISE AWKWARD PAGE TURNS
AND TO MAKE PLAYING FROM IT A REAL PLEASURE.
PARTICULAR CARE HAS BEEN GIVEN TO SPECIFYING ACID-FREE,
NEUTRAL-SIZED PAPER MADE FROM PULPS WHICH HAVE NOT BEEN
ELEMENTAL CHLORINE BLEACHED. THIS PULP IS FROM FARMED
SUSTAINABLE FORESTS AND WAS PRODUCED WITH SPECIAL REGARD
FOR THE ENVIRONMENT.
THROUGHOUT, THE PRINTING AND BINDING HAVE BEEN PLANNED
TO ENSURE A STURDY, ATTRACTIVE PUBLICATION WHICH SHOULD
GIVE YEARS OF ENJOYMENT.
IF YOUR COPY FAILS TO MEET OUR HIGH STANDARDS,
PLEASE INFORM US AND WE WILL GLADLY REPLACE IT.

BEAUTIFUL

Every day is so wonderful
Then suddenly it's hard to breathe
Now and then I get insecure
From all the pain, I'm so ashamed

I am beautiful no matter what they say
Words can't bring me down
I am beautiful in every single way
Words can't bring me down
So don't you bring me down today

To all your friends you're delirious
You're so consumed in all your doom
You're trying hard to fill the emptiness
The pieces gone, left the puzzle undone
That's the way it is

You are beautiful no matter what they say
Words can't bring you down
You are beautiful in every single way
Words can't bring you down
So don't you bring me down today

No matter what we do
No matter what we say
There's a song inside the tune
Full of beautiful mistakes

And everywhere we go
The sun will always shine
But tomorrow we might awake
on the other side

'Cause we are beautiful no matter what they say
Words won't bring us down
We are beautiful in every single way
Yes, words can't bring us down
So don't you bring me down today, oh, today
Don't you bring me down today

CANDYMAN

Tarzan and Jane were swinging on a vine
Candyman, candyman
Sippin' from a bottle of Vodka double wine
Sweet sugar candyman, ah hey, yeah

I met him out for dinner on a Friday night
He really had me workin' up an appetite
He had tattoos up and down his arm
There's nothing more dangerous than a boy with charm

He's a one-stop shop, makes the panties drop
He's a sweet talking sugar coated candyman
A sweet talking sugar coated candyman, oh, yeah

He took me to the Spider Club at Hollywood and Vine
We drank champagne and we danced all night
We shook the paparazzi for a big surprise
The gossip tonight will be tomorrow's headlines

He's a one-stop shop, makes my cherry pop
He's a sweet talking sugar coated candyman
A sweet talking sugar coated candyman

Vocal ad lib.

He's a one-stop shop, makes my cherry pop
He's a sweet talking sugar coated candyman
A sweet talking sugar coated candyman, ah hey, yeah

Well by now I'm getting all bothered and hot
When he kissed my mouth he really hit the spot
He had lips like sugar cane
Good things come for boys who wait

Tarzan and Jane were swinging on a vine
Candyman, candyman
Sippin' from a bottle of Vodka double wine
Candyman, candyman

Sweet sugar, candyman
He's a one-stop, gotcha hot, makin' all the panties drop
Sweet sugar, candyman
He's a one-stop, got me hot, makin' my "ah" hot
Sweet sugar, Candyman
He's a one stop, get it while it's hot, baby don't stop
Sweet sugar

He got those lips like sugar cane
Good things come for boys who wait

He's a one-stop shop with a real big "ah."
He's a sweet talking sugar coated candyman
A sweet talking sugar coated candyman
A sweet talking sugar coated candyman
A sweet talking sugar coated candyman

Candyman, candyman, candyman, candyman
Candyman, candyman, candyman, candyman

Tarzan and Jane were swinging on a vine
(Tarzan and Jane were swinging on a vine)
Sippin' from a bottle of Vodka double wine
(Sippin' from a bottle of Vodka double wine)

Jane lost her grip and a-down she fell
(Jane lost her grip and a-down she fell)
Squared herself away as she let out a yell
(Squared herself away as she let out a yell)

FIGHTER

After all you put me through
You'd think I'd despise you
But in the end I wanna thank you
'Cause you made me that much stronger

Well I thought I knew you
thinkin' that you were true
Guess I, I couldn't trust, called your bluff
Time is up 'cause I've had enough

You were there by my side
Always down for the ride
But your joyride just came down in flames
'Cause your greed sold me out in shame, mm

After all of the stealing and cheating
You probably think that
I hold resentment for you
But uh, uh, oh no, you're wrong

'Cause if it wasn't for all that you tried to do
I wouldn't know just how capable I am to pull through
So I wanna say thank you

'Cause it makes me that much stronger
Makes me work a little bit harder
It makes me that much wiser
So thanks for making me a fighter
Made me learn a little bit faster
Made my skin a little bit thicker
It makes me that much smarter
So thanks for making me a fighter

Oh, oh, oh, oh, oh, eh, eh, oh

Never saw it coming
All of your back stabbing
Just so you could cash in on a good thing
Before I'd realise your game

I heard you're going round
Playin' the victim now
But don't even begin feeling I'm the one to blame
'Cause you dug your own grave

After all of the fights and the lies
'Cause you're wanting to haunt me
But that don't work any more
No more, uh, uh, it's over

'Cause if it wasn't for all of your torture
I wouldn't know how to be this way now
And never back down
So I wanna say thank you

Chorus

How could this man I thought I knew
Turn out to be unjust, so cruel
Could only see the good in you
Pretended not to see the truth

You tried to hide your lies
Disguise yourself through
Living in denial
But in the end you'll see
You won't stop me

I am a fighter and I, I ain't gonna stop
There is no turning back, I've had enough

Chorus

Thought I wouldn't forget
Thought I, I remember, yes
I remember, I remember

Thought I wouldn't forget
Thought I, I remember, yes
I remember, I remember

Chorus

GENIE IN A BOTTLE

C'mon, c'mon, mm yeah, oh, ooh, oh mm
I feel like I've been locked up tight
For a century of lonely nights
Waiting for someone
To release me

You're lickin' your lips and blowin' kisses my way
But that don't mean I'm gonna give it away
Baby, baby, baby

Oh, my body's saying let's go
Oh, but my heart is saying no, no

If you wanna be with me
Baby, there's a price to pay
I'm a genie in a bottle
You gotta rub me the right way

If you wanna be with me
I can make your wish come true
You gotta make a big impression
Gotta like what you do

I'm a genie in a bottle, baby
You gotta rub me the right way, honey
I'm a genie in a bottle, baby
Come, come, come on and let me out

Music's playing and the light's down low
Just one more dance and then we're good to go
Waiting for someone
Who needs me

Hormones racing at the speed of light
But that don't mean it's gotta be tonight
Baby, baby, baby

Oh, my body's saying let's go
Oh, but my heart is saying no, no

If you wanna be with me
Baby, there's a price to pay
I'm a genie in a bottle
You gotta rub me the right way

If you wanna be with me
I can make your wish come true
Just come and set me free, baby
And I'll be with you

I'm a genie in a bottle, baby
You gotta rub me the right way, honey
I'm a genie in a bottle, baby
Come, come, come on and let me out

I'm a genie in a bottle, baby
You gotta rub me the right way, honey
I'm a genie in a bottle, baby
Come, come, come on and let me out

Oh, my body's saying let's go
Oh, but my heart is saying no, no

If you wanna be with me
Baby, there's a price to pay
I'm a genie in a bottle
You gotta rub me the right way

If you wanna be with me
I can make your wish come true
You gotta make a big impression
You gotta like what you do

If you wanna be with me
Baby, there's a price to pay
I'm a genie in a bottle
You gotta rub me the right way

If you wanna be with me
I can make your wish come true
Just come and set me free, baby
And I'll be with you

I'm a genie in a bottle, baby
Come, come, come on and let me out

HURT

Seems like it was yesterday
When I saw your face
You told me how proud you were
But I walked away
If only I knew
What I know today, ooh, ooh

I would hold you in my arms
I would take the pain away
Thank you for all you've done
Forgive all your mistakes
There's nothing I wouldn't do
To hear your voice again
Sometimes I wanna call you
But I know you won't be there

Whoa, I'm sorry for
Blaming you
For everything
I just couldn't do
And I've hurt myself
By hurting you

Some days I feel broke inside
But I won't admit it
Sometimes I just wanna hide
'Cause it's you I miss
And it's so hard to say goodbye
When it comes to this, ooh

Would you tell me I was wrong
Would you help me understand
Are you looking down upon me
Are you proud of who I am
There's nothing I wouldn't do
To have just one more chance
To look into your eyes
And see you looking back

Whoa, I'm sorry for
Blaming you
For everything
I just couldn't do
And I've hurt myself, oh

If I had just one more day
I would tell you how much that I've missed you
Since you've been away

Oh, it's dangerous
It's so out of line
To try and turn back time

I'm sorry for
Blaming you
For everything
I just couldn't do
And I've hurt myself
By hurting you

THE VOICE WITHIN

Young girl, don't cry
I'll be right here when your world starts to fall, ooh
Young girl, it's alright
Your tears will dry, you'll soon be free to fly, ooh

When you're safe inside your room, you tend to dream
Of a place where nothing's harder than it seems
No one ever wants or bothers to explain
Of the heartache life can bring and what it means

When there's no one else, look inside yourself
Like your oldest friend, just trust the voice within
Then you'll find the strength that will guide your way
If you'll learn to begin to trust the voice within

Young girl, don't hide
You'll never change if you just run away, ooh
Young girl, just hold tight
Soon you're gonna see your brighter day, ooh

Now, in a world where innocence is quickly claimed
It's so hard to stand your ground when you're so afraid
No one reaches out a hand for you to hold
When you look outside, look inside to your soul

When there's no one else, look inside yourself
Like your oldest friend, just trust the voice within
Then you'll find the strength that will guide your way
If you'll learn to begin to trust the voice within

(Ooh, ooh, ooh, ooh)

Life is a journey
It can take you anywhere you choose to go
And long as you're learning
You'll find all you'll ever need to know

When there's no one else, look inside yourself
Like your oldest friend, just trust the voice within
Then you'll find the strength that will guide your way
If you'll learn to begin to trust the voice within

Young girl, don't cry
I'll be right here when your world starts to fall
Ooh, mm

BEAUTIFUL

WORDS & MUSIC BY LINDA PERRY

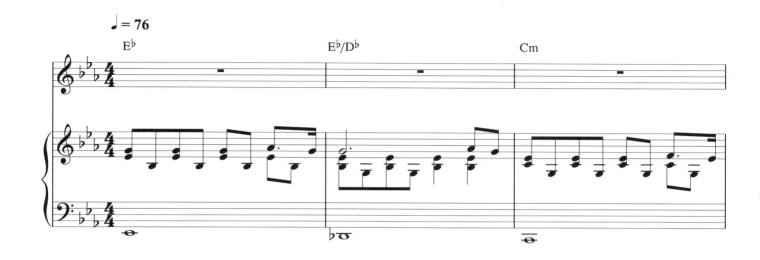

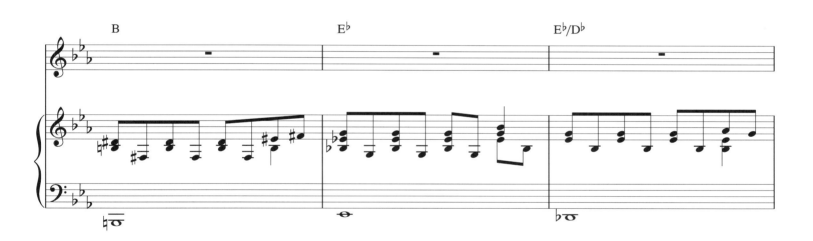

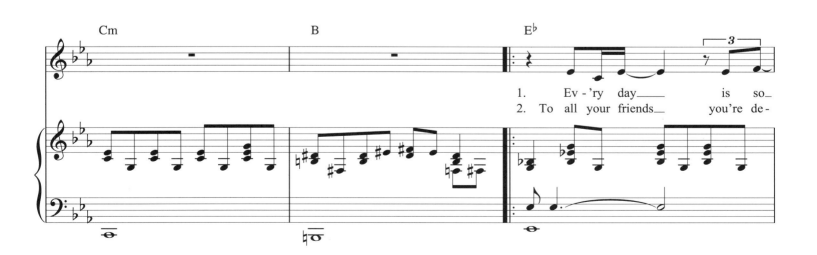

1. Ev -'ry day___ is so___
2. To all your friends___ you're de-

Words can't bring me down.
2° you
3° won't bring us

I am beautiful in
2° You are
3° we are

ev-'ry sin-gle way.

Words can't bring me down.
2° you
3° us

So don't you bring me down to-day.

9

Coda

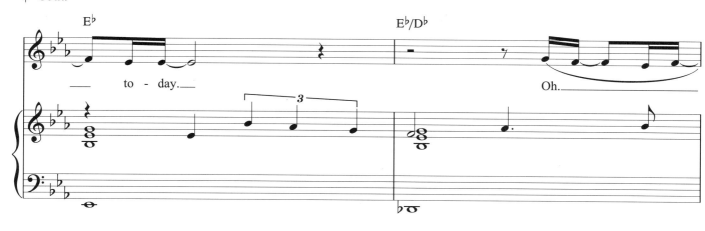

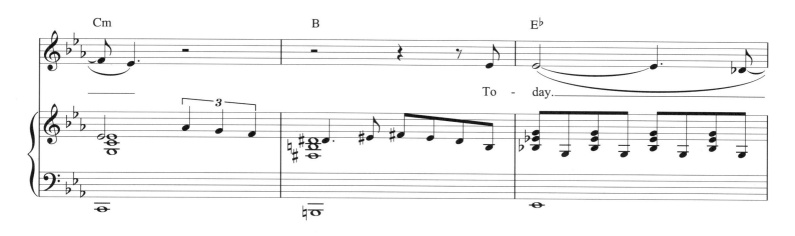

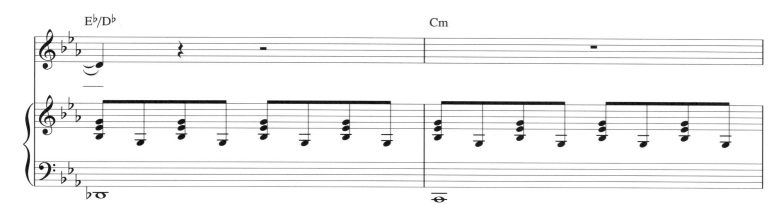

Free time

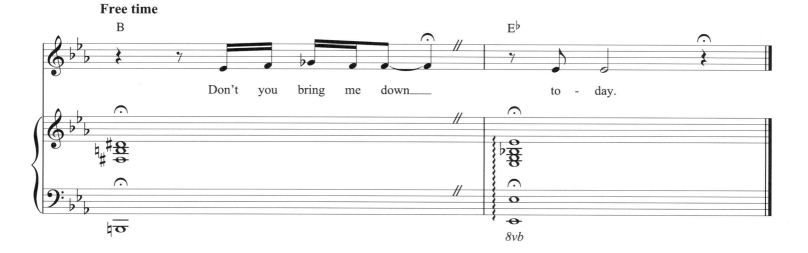

11

CANDYMAN

WORDS & MUSIC BY CHRISTINA AGUILERA & LINDA PERRY

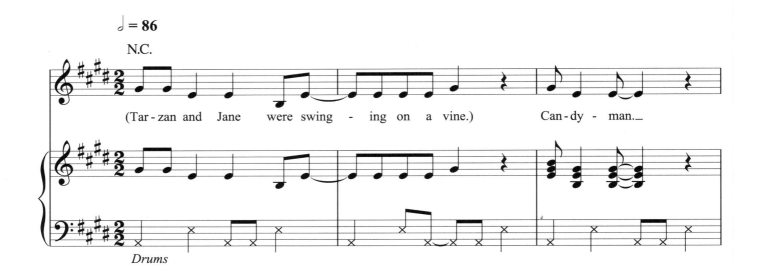

(Tar-zan and Jane were swing - ing on a vine.) Can-dy-man.

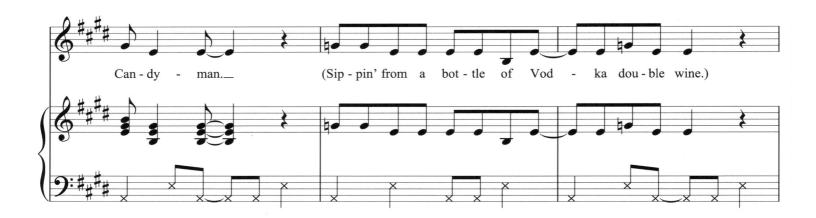

Can-dy - man. (Sip-pin' from a bot-tle of Vod - ka dou-ble wine.)

Sweet su-gar. Can-dy-man. Ah hey,

D.S. al Coda

15

18

(Sip - pin' from a bot - tle of Vod - ka dou-ble wine.) *(Chorus)* (Sip - pin' from a bot - tle of Vod -

- ka dou-ble wine.) (Jane lost her grip and a - down she fell.)

(Chorus) (Jane lost her grip and a - down she fell.)__ (Squared her-self a - way as she

let out a yell.) *(Chorus)*(Squared her-self a - way as she let out a yell.)

FIGHTER

WORDS & MUSIC BY CHRISTINA AGUILERA & SCOTT STORCH

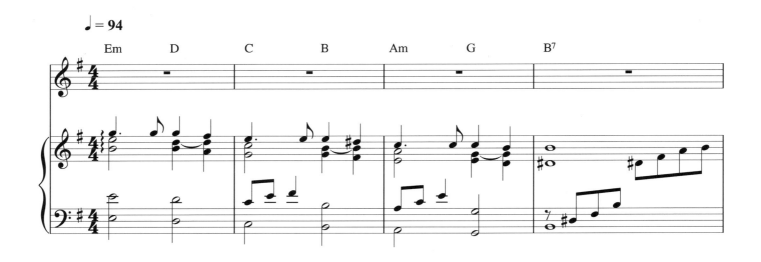

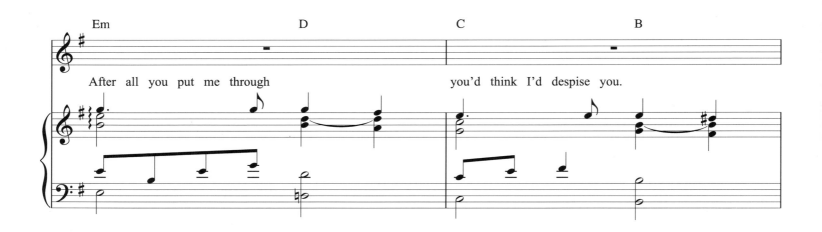

After all you put me through you'd think I'd despise you.

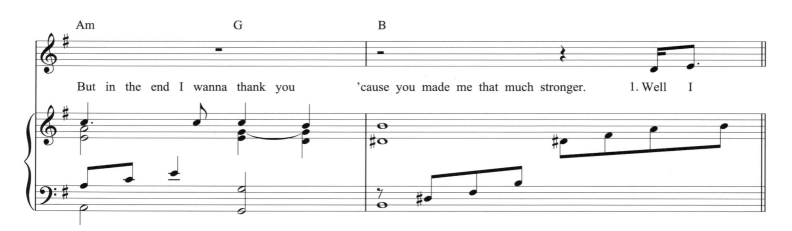

But in the end I wanna thank you 'cause you made me that much stronger. 1. Well I

D.S. al Coda

CODA

27

GENIE IN A BOTTLE

WORDS & MUSIC BY STEVE KIPNER, DAVID FRANK & PAMELA SHEYNE

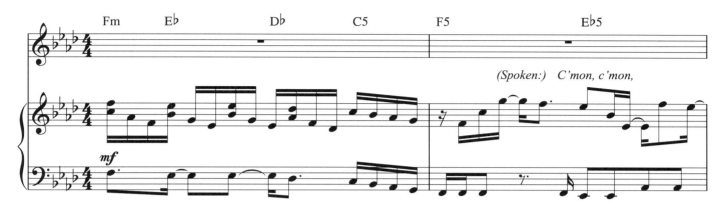

Oh. _____ But my heart is say-ing no, no.

If you wan-na be with me, ba-by, there's a price to pay. I'm a ge-nie in a bot-

-tle; you got-ta rub me the right way. If you wan-na be with

me, I can make your wish come true. You got-ta make a big im-pres-

-sion. Got - ta like what you do. I'm a ge - nie in a bot - tle, ba - by.

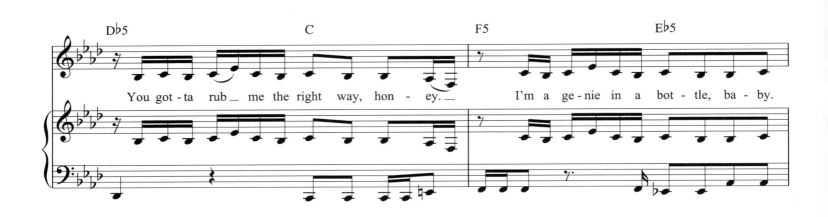

You got - ta rub _ me the right way, hon - ey. _ I'm a ge - nie in a bot - tle, ba - by.

Come, _ come, come on and let me out. true. Just come and set _ me free, _

_ ba - by, _ and I'll be with you. _ I'm a ge - nie in a bot - tle, ba - by.

My bod-y's say-ing let's go. Oh. _____

But my heart is say-ing no, no. If you wan-na be with

me, ba - by, there's a price to pay. I'm a ge - nie in a bot-

- tle. You got - ta rub me the right way. If you wan - na be with

HURT

WORDS & MUSIC BY LINDA PERRY,
CHRISTINA AGUILERA & MARK RONSON

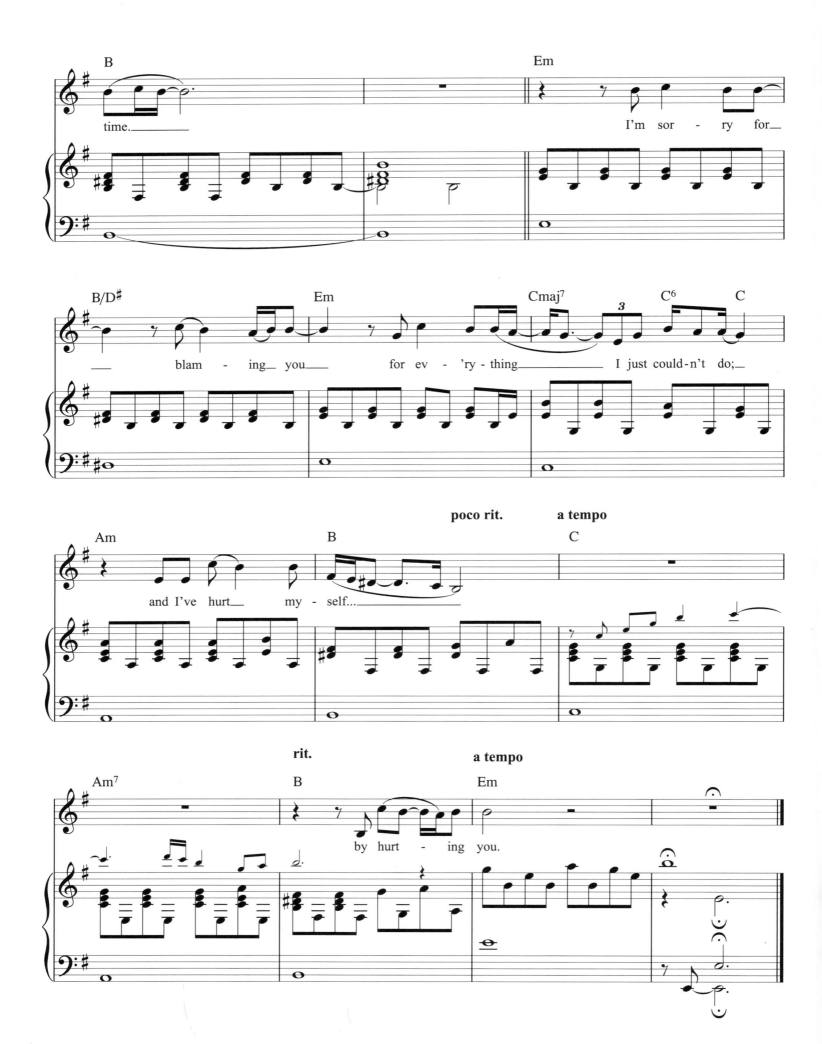

THE VOICE WITHIN

WORDS & MUSIC BY CHRISTINA AGUILERA
& GLEN BALLARD

45

CD Backing Tracks

1. Beautiful
(Perry) Sony/ATV Harmony (UK) Limited

2. Candyman
(Aguilera/Perry) Sony/ATV Harmony (UK) Limited/
Universal Music Publishing International Limited/Universal Music Publishing MGB Limited

3. Fighter
(Aguilera/Storch) Universal Music Publishing International Limited/Cherry Lane Music Limited

4. Genie In A Bottle
(Kipner/Frank/Sheyne) EMI Music Publishing Limited/Appletree Songs Limited

5. Hurt
(Perry/Aguilera/Ronson) Sony/ATV Harmony (UK) Limited/Universal Music Publishing
International Limited/Universal Music Publishing MGB Limited/EMI Music Publishing Limited

6. The Voice Within
(Aguilera/Ballard) Universal/MCA Music Limited/Universal Music Publishing
International Limited